PROOF READING ACTIVITI

PHOTOCOPIABLE MASTERS

# BE THE
# TEACHER
# BOOK
# 2

Spelling Made

*Easy* SERIES

Corresponding to Spelling Made Easy
Level 2 and Level 3

**Best Selling Series by**
# Violet Brand

**Published by**  ***Brand*** *Books*

**BrandBooks, England**

*Be the Teacher* Book Two.  First published in the United Kingdom in 1996
by Egon Publishers Ltd.


Original copyright © Egon Publishers Ltd
and Violet Brand, 1996
ISBN 1 899998 06 3

Copyright assigned to BrandBooks
(a division of G & M Brand Publications Ltd) and Violet Brand 2002

ISBN 1-904421-09-1

# BE THE TEACHER

# Introduction

Proof reading is an essential part of written English – and the hardest work to proof read is your own. Therefore these sheets will hopefully enable children to develop skills by proof reading the work of others.

The mistakes within the passages are not random, but specifically related to the work covered in *Spelling Made Easy*, from the introductory Level to Level 3. Following the marking, both teachers and children will be aware of word families, individual words and aspects of punctuation which need to be re-taught and reinforced. The children might also have been reminded that punctuation is part of meaning. Through the absence of full stops or question marks, the reader has been unsure of the intended meaning of the writer.

For some children, the following guidelines might be helpful in connection with *Be The Teacher*, but also with their own written work.

## Guidelines

(a) Read through the passage aloud for meaning. Do not let the eyes just glide over it.

(b) Read with a pencil/ball point pen in the hand, following each word as it is read. This will help the student to spot words that have been omitted because the voice alone may put these in and the eyes will be deceived.

(c) The voice and the pencil will falter if the punctuation is wrong. Punctuation is a vital part of meaning.

(d) Re-read for spelling errors. Hopefully, warning bells will ring over wrong spellings and misuse of words. Even if corrections cannot be made, the spotting of errors is a good sign and should be encouraged.

As the mistakes are not their own but those of the pupils of Brand's Patch School, the children will hopefully enjoy the work and will become increasingly aware of their own weaknesses.

The weaknesses of individual children will be revealed by the corrections that are not in red!

# Index

# Introduction for the
# Brand's Patch School teachers

You are now the teachers at Brand's Patch School and you will have to mark the pieces of work that the children write. Like all teachers, you can use a red pencil (or ball point pen).

Some of the children will make spelling mistakes. Will you spot all of the words they get wrong? Will you be able to write the words correctly with your red pen? Will you notice the speech marks and capital letters that are missing?

Remember, if full stops or question marks are left out, you might be puzzled about what the writer is trying to say.

When you have finished your marking with the red pen, you will probably want to know whether you spotted all of the mistakes. Your teacher will give you another sheet of the same work, with the corrections made.

The question is, were there any mistakes you missed?

The bilding was dilaperdated and the teechers new that they could not safley accomerdate the school students in it. They was desparate and sent an anxcus messege back to their headmarster.

He asked if it was possable for them all to stay in seperate accommerdation. But as it was quiet late at night it seemed impossable to find enywhere else. After more discussion they decided to stay until the morning and hopped they would be fortunat.

The teachers gave the students hot choclate made with evaperated milk and a biscit. Then they persaded them to go to bed – and to sleep.

# 1. Annie Andrews — Monday, September 21st

The bilding was dilaperdated and the teechers new that they
*(building, dilapidated, teachers knew)*

could not safley accomerdate the school students in it. They was
*(safely accommodate, were)*

desparate and sent an anxcus messege back to their
*(desperate, anxious message)*

headmarster.
*(headmaster.)*

He asked if it was possable for them all to stay in seperate
*(possible, separate)*

accommerdation. But as it was quiet late at night it seemed
*(accommodation. quite)*

impossable to find enywhere else. After more discussion they
*(impossible, anywhere)*

decided to stay until the morning and hopped they would be
*(hoped)*

fortunat.
*(fortunate.)*

The teachers gave the students hot choclate made with
*(chocolate)*

evaperated milk and a biscit. Then they persaded them to go to
*(evaporated, biscuit. persuaded)*

bed - and to sleep.

## Did you notice every mistake?

Do you think that Annie was one of the students? Perhaps she was just writing a story. But did you notice that she made quite a lot of mistakes with words in the new 'a-e' family?

If you missed any of them, look very hard at that family in your word book — especially the 'tricky bits'. Then correct those words with your coloured pencil (not red).

In ninteen nintey four it seemed likley that there would at last be piece in Northern Irland. The Prim Minsters of the United Kindom and of Irland held talks. Poeple from Nother Irland went to Amerca to have discussion and the newpapers in many countries were full of reports.

Fear of bombs and shoting begun to evaperate in england and in northern ireland. evryone hopped that the talks would continue and the guns would be throwed away, so that at last saftey would return  their towns and citys.

*nineteen ninety*                        *likely*
In ninteen nintey four it seemed likley that there would at last
*peace*          *Ireland.*     *Prime Ministers*
be piece in Northern Irland. The Prim Minsters of the United
*Kingdom*          *Ireland*              *People*        *Northern Ireland*
Kindom and of Irland held talks. Poeple from Nother Irland went
*America*                *discussions*                *newspapers*
to Amerca to have discussion and the newpapers in many

countries were full of reports.
                         *shooting began    evaporate    England*
. Fear of bombs and shoting begun to evaperate in england and
*Northern Ireland. Everyone hoped*
in northern ireland. evryone hopped that the talks would
                                            *thrown*
continue and the guns would be throwed away, so that at last
*safety*              *to*                    *cities.*
saftey would return ∧ their towns and citys.

## Did you notice every mistake?

Bill is certainly aware of the changes that are taking place in <u>Ireland</u>.

He will need to look very carefully at that word. Did you spot the mistake - and all the others? If you missed any, think hard about them, then correct with your other coloured pencil.

In some parts of the country cliffs begin to erod because of the constant battering of the sea. as more and more of the land collapse the owner of hotls motls find themselves near and near to the ege of the cliff. They feel hopless and desprate. There is nothink they can do to prevent this horible disturbance to their live.

Some people pack their cloths and just go. Gradully there are fewer and fewer man, woman and childrn living in the zone. Those that are left become very lonly as they wait for the cliff to erod.

In some parts of the country cliffs begin to *erode* erod because of

the constant battering of the sea. *As* as more and more of the land

*collapses* *owners* *hotels and motels* *nearer* collapse the owner of hotls ∧ motls find themselves near and

*nearer* *edge* *hopeless* *desperate.* near to the ege of the cliff. They feel hopless and desprate. There

*nothing* *horrible* is nothink they can do to prevent this horible disturbance to

*lives.* their live.

*clothes* *Gradually* Some people pack their cloths and just go. Gradully there are

*men, women* *children* fewer and fewer man, woman and childrn living in the zone.

*lonely* Those that are left become very lonly as they wait for the cliff to

*erode.* erod.

## Did you notice every mistake?

Carole captures in words how people feel when this terrible thing happens to them.

Did you manage to correct all of her mistakes? If you missed any think carefully about those words, so that you do not make the same errors. Then take your coloured pencil (not red) and make the corrections.

Fifty year ago it was thought that there were no substute for coal. It was usd for fire in houses to provide heat for warth and cooking. Usully there was only one fir in a house, no heat in the bedroms and a second living room was not usd in cold wether.

Coal was also usd to make gas and elctricity so the coal-miner worked hard make shore that there was enuff coal for all of the consumers.

Now, things has changd. To make gas and elctricity coal is not needed. Most people dont use coal to heat their homes or to do the cooking. Meny coal-mine have closd and there is a acut shortag of jobs for miners.

*years* *was* *substitute*
Fifty year ago it was thought that there were no substute for

*used* *fires* *warmth*
coal. It was usd for fire in houses to provide heat for warth and

*Usually* *fire*
cooking. Usully there was only one fir in a house, no heat in the

*bedrooms* *used* *weather.*
bedroms and a second living room was not usd in cold wether.

*used* *electricity*
Coal was also usd to make gas and elctricity so the

*coal-miners* *to* *sure* *enough*
coal-miner worked hard ∧ make shore that there was enuff coal

for all of the consumers.

*have changed.* *electricity*
Now, things has changd. To make gas and elctricity coal is

*don't*
not needed. Most people dont use coal to heat their homes or to

*Many coal-mines* *closed* *an acute*
do the cooking. Meny coal-mine have closd and there is a acut

*shortage*
shortag of jobs for miners.

## Did you notice every mistake?

All of the children so far are writing the date correctly. That is good.

David will need to look again at the words in his new 'u-e' family and think very carefully about them.

Did you spot and correct all of his errors? If you missed any, think hard as you use your coloured pencil to correct them.

It was very fogy in the valey at the begining of the week and the visiters from europe were very disapointed. It was august and they were expeting the wether to be beatifully warm, even in England. Gradully the fog began to clear and by Wensday morning the sun was shinning.

They had a discussion with some friend on the telphone who recomended a boat excersion up the river. This was a tremndous trip from begining to end. They were definitly not disapointed.

_foggy      valley        beginning_
It was very fogy in the valey at the begining of the week and
_visitors      Europe          disappointed.        August_
the visiters from europe were very disapointed. It was august
_expecting    weather      beautifully_
and they were expeting the wether to be beatifully warm, even in
_Gradually                              Wednesday_
England. Gradully the fog began to clear and by Wensday
_shining._
morning the sun was shinning.

_friends        telephone_
They had a discussion with some friend on the telphone who
_recommended          excursion                        tremendous_
recomended a boat excersion up the river. This was a tremndous
_beginning                      definitely    disappointed._
trip from begining to end. They were definitly not disapointed.

## Did you notice every mistake?

Emily does not seem to remember that, in a lot of words, you have to double the consonant to keep the vowel short.

She will have to look at her word family book again and <u>listen</u> to the sounds she needs to make in these words. Then she might remember next time she needs to use them.

Did you spot all of her mistakes? If not, you had better look at that word family again. She also forgot the capital letters for <u>Europe</u> and <u>August</u>. I am sure you made those corrections.

In the suberbs of many large citys burgleries hapen evry night – and sometimes during the day. It is a very narsty suprise for people to arive home from work to find that there house has been bergled.

The plice are trying desprately to pursu the burglars and cope with the problems. But its imposible to know where the next burgleries will ocur. They reqest the public to help by makeing sure that houses is loked and secur. People are also asked to definitly watch the house of their nieghbours.

suburbs                    cities burglaries happen every
In the suberbs of many large citys burgleries hapen evry

nasty surprise
night – and sometimes during the day. It is a very narsty suprise

arrive                                        their
for people to arive home from work to find that there house has

burgled.
been bergled.

police            desperately    pursue
The plice are trying desprately to pursu the burglars and cope

it's impossible
with the problems. But its imposible to know where the next

burglaries        occur.        request                        making
burgleries will ocur. They reqest the public to help by makeing

are locked      secure.
sure that houses is loked and secur. People are also asked to

definitely                houses            neighbours.
definitly watch the house of their nieghbours.

# Did you notice every mistake?

Fiona has probably been reading about <u>burglaries</u> in the newspaper, or hearing about them on the News.

She will need to look at the 'ur' family again in her word book.

Did you notice those mistakes – and the others? If you missed any, think very carefully and correct them with your coloured pen (not red).

There have been objetions to the altertions being made to the staton, as these have definitly affected the acomodation for young peopel. Meny live in this large town in order to continu their educatoin. But it is becoming hard and hard for them to find the acomodation they reqire.

This sitution has ocurred because the old dilaperdated houses by the station, are being knoked down so that the station can be made biger. Rents for newer flats and house in the town are to xpensive for the students. Preperation of other cheaper acomodation near the colleges definitly recomended.

*objections      alterations*
There have been objetions to the altertions being made to the
*station,          definitely        accommodation*
staton, as these have definitly affected the acomodation for
*people. Many                                    continue*
young peopel. Meny live in this large town in order to continu
*education.              harder   harder*
their educatoin. But it is becoming hard and hard for them to
*accommodation     require.*
find the acomodation they reqire.
*situation    occurred                    dilapidated*
This sitution has ocurred because the old dilaperdated houses
*knocked*
by the station, are being knoked down so that the station can be
*bigger.                        houses              too*
made biger. Rents for newer flats and house in the town are to
*expensive              Preparation*
xpensive for the students. Preperation of other cheaper
*accommodation                is definitely recommended.*
acomodation near the colleges ʌ definitly recomended.

## Did you notice every mistake?

A thoughtful piece of writing with some spelling mistakes.

Did you spot them all? If you did not, think <u>very</u> carefully about the ones you missed, as you take your pencil (not red) to correct them.

There are usully noticable changes in the perfmance of football teams after they have had a good practise. They are more likly to suceed and win maches if the early preperation has been good.

Excitment grows amongst a teams suporters with the repitition of wins and the team remain unbeaten. Preperation is also important for the secnd team in case a good play has an acident during the game and a replacment is needed.

If there is not another player to suceed him, then sucess will not continu.

## 8. Helen Hicks — Wednesday, September 30th

usually noticeable performance
There are usully noticable changes in the perfmance of
practice.
football teams after they have had a good practise. They are
likely succeed matches preparation
more likly to suceed and win maches if the early preperation has
been good.

Excitement team's supporters
Excitment grows amongst a teams suporters with the
repetition remains Preparation
repitition of wins and the team remain unbeaten. Preperation is
second player
also important for the secnd team in case a good play has an
accident replacement
acident during the game and a replacment is needed.

succeed success
If there is not another player to suceed him, then sucess will
continue.
not continu.

## Did you notice every mistake?

Helen certainly knows a great deal about football teams and what helps them to win.

Did you correct all of the errors? If not think hard about the words you missed so that you do not make the same mistakes. Correct with your coloured pencil.

I went on the Chanel Tunel train with my grandma to paris on Saterday. Going to France from Waterloo in london was a great sucess and I was exsited. We travel through Kent at a great speed and then arrive at the Chunnel at about half past elven. The sun was shinning and the whether was warm. Lights shone at each side the train and we zomed into the darkness Chunnel.

Grandma had booked acomodation in Paris and we had a great time. When we come back on sunday, evrything was much more dificult.

## 9. Ian Instone                    Thursday, October 1st

Channel Tunnel                                    Paris
I went on the Chanel Tunel train with my grandma to paris on
Saturday.                                    London
Saterday. Going to France from Waterloo in london was a
    success          excited   travelled
great sucess and I was exsited. We travel through Kent at a great
        arrived                              eleven.
speed and then arrive at the Chunnel at about half past elven.
        shining          weather
The sun was shinning and the whether was warm. Lights shone
        of              zoomed              of the
at each side∧the train and we zomed into the darkness∧Chunnel.
            accommodation
Grandma had booked acomodation in Paris and we had a
            came        Sunday, everything
great time. When we come back on sunday, evrything was much
    difficult.
more dificult.

# Did you notice every mistake?

That was a wonderful treat for Ian and he is quite right to call it the
Chunnel. It was not his spelling that was wrong. But there were other
mistakes.

Did you spot them all?

I will not exagerate the dificulties the pasengers on our train had when we come back from Paris on sunday. My story will be truthfull.

We arived at the staton in plenty of time after a wonderfull time. Then we stood whith the other pasengers and waited to get the train. We waited and waited people began to get anoyed with the delay. Finally their was a mesage to say that the train had engine falure and could'nt take us. Latter we had go on three diffrent trains to get on a tunel train at Lille.

On that train there was no hot food and only drinks was free coke and water. That was delightfull for me – I like coke – but not for Gradma and lot of other pasengers. We arived at Waterloo nealy three ours late. Dad was still waiting. That was briliant.

*exaggerate   difficulties   passengers*
I will not exagerate the dificulties the pasengers on our train
*came*                              *Sunday.*
had when we come back from Paris on sunday. My story will be
*truthful*
truthfull.
*arrived        station                              wonderful*
We arived at the staton in plenty of time after a wonderfull
*with              passengers*
time. Then we stood whith the other pasengers and waited to
*on                                      People*
get∧the train. We waited and waited. people began to get
*annoyed                        there        message*
anoyed with the delay. Finally their was a mesage to say that
*failure        couldn't            Later*
the train had engine falure and could'nt take us. Latter we
*to          different                    tunnel*
had∧go on three diffrent trains to get on a tunel train at Lille.
*the              were*
On that train there was no hot food and∧only drinks was free
*delightful*
coke and water. That was delightfull for me – I like coke – but
*Grandma    a              passengers.    arrived*
not for Gradma and∧lot of other pasengers. We arived at
*nearly      hours*
Waterloo nealy three ours late. Dad was still waiting. That was
*brilliant.*
briliant.

## Did you notice every mistake?

The journey home from Paris was obviously difficult, but I am sure that Ian enjoyed the free coke.

He is still having difficulties with some of his word families.

Did you notice which ones – and make the corrections?

If you missed any mistakes, think very hard as you use your coloured pencil to write the words correctly.

I had a very bad stomack acke last night. It was really painfull. Fortunatly my father is a chemit and he were abel to get the right medcine for me. This morning I feelt much beter and was able to come school. I am glad because at dinner time today we have chir practise and my brother Chistopher will be playing the piano accompanment. The music is really beatiful.

We have another for weeks of preperation and then the school chior is going in for a musick competitoin and we hope we will win.

stomach ache
I had a very bad stomack acke last night. It was really
painful. Fortunately          chemist        was able
painfull. Fortunatly my father is a chemit and he were abel to get
medicine                     felt        better
the right medcine for me. This morning I feelt much beter and
to
was able to come ˄ school. I am glad because at dinner time
choir practice              Christopher
today we have chir practise and my brother Chistopher will be
accompaniment.              beautiful.
playing the piano accompanment. The music is really beatiful.
four        preparation
We have another for weeks of preperation and then the
choir          music  competition
school chior is going in for a musick competitoin and we hope we

will win.

## Did you notice every mistake?

Jessica certainly enjoys singing in the choir and is looking forward to the music competition.

I think she should look very carefully at those two words – <u>choir</u> and <u>music</u> – so that when she writes about them, she can spell the words correctly.

Did you spot her mistakes? Think hard about those you missed and then use your other coloured pencil to correct them.

26 Dover Street
London W6
6.10.96

Dere Grandad,

We is doing the second Werld War as our class topic this term. Natrally, we are find it very intresting.

Our teacher has us to wite to members of our famly asking them for their recolections of the war. I know you was a tenager at that time hopfully, you will be able to rember some of the things that hapened.

Would you like to sit down quitely and write down what you rember? Or would you like me to come see you so that we can talk about the war

Lots of love

Katy

26 Dover Street
London W6
6.10.96

Dere Grandad,

*Dear*

We is doing the second Werld War as our class topic this
*are*          *Second World*

term. Natrally, we are find it very intresting.
*Naturally,*     *finding*     *interesting.*

Our teacher has ∧ us to wite to members of our famly asking
*told*     *write*                              *family*

them for their recolections of the war. I know you was a tenager
*recollections*                              *were   teenager*

at that time. hopfully, you will be able to rember some of the
*Hopefully,*                    *remember*

things that hapened.
*happened.*

Would you like to sit down quitely and write down what you
*quietly*

rember? Or would you like me to come ∧ see you so that we can
*remember*                              *to*

talk about the war?

Lots of love

Katy

## Did you notice every mistake?

Katy's teacher at Brand's Patch School knew that all of the children in the class would learn a lot about the Second World War from people who were alive then.

I am sure that Katy's grandad would have been so delighted to receive the letter, that he would not have been worried about her spelling mistakes.

Did you spot them all? If you missed any, think very hard about the correct spellings and then write the words with your coloured pencil (not red).

25

In histry we are doing the Second World War and in geograpy we have been look at counties near the equater. Here there is carniverous anmals and the tempratures are very high. I do not think I would like to live in one of those counties.

My cousins live in singapore for about five year. They say it was very hot and sticky when you was out in the steets. But if you were fortnate and were rich, your house and school was cool. Praps the poor people who was born there were usd to the climat.

history
In histry we are doing the Second World War and in

looking  countries          equator.
geograpy we have been look at counties near the equater. Here

are carnivorous animals        temperatures
there is carniverous anmals and the tempratures are very high.

countries.
I do not think I would like to live in one of those counties.

lived  Singapore              years.
My cousins live in singapore for about five year. They say it

were          streets.
was very hot and sticky when you was out in the steets. But if

fortunate                              were
you were fortnate and were rich, your house and school was

Perhaps              were          used
cool. Praps the poor people who was born there were usd to the
climate.
climat.


## Did you notice every mistake?

Linda will need to look very carefully at countries and counties. Also, she should look at country and county, say the words aloud and hear the differences in the sounds within the words.

She will also need to think about what a country is — and in England, what a county is.

Did you spot these mistakes — and others? If you missed any, think very carefully as you correct.

For our homework last night we had to right a list of things you can cut with. The telvision was on. It was a good programme and I didn't want to miss it, so I lisened as I rote.

These are the words I rote —

sord

nife                    naw

sisors                  saw

Some of my spelling were rong and my teacher was not pleased, particul when she new I was watching TV as I was writting. She did not think that to naw meant to cut. But I was thinking about the teef of our dog. He don't need a nife to cut up his diner. He just naws threw the meat.

_write_
For our homework last night we had to right a list of things
_television_
you can cut with. The telvision was on. It was a good
_listened_     _wrote._
programme and I didn't want to miss it, so I lisened as I rote.
_wrote_
These are the words I rote —

_sword_
sord
_knife_          _gnaw_
nife          naw
_scissors_
sisors          saw

_spellings_     _wrong_
Some of my spelling were rong and my teacher was not
_particularly_          _knew_
pleased, particul when she new I was watching TV as I was
_writing_                    _gnaw_
writting. She did not think that to naw meant to cut. But I was
_teeth_          _doesn't_     _knife_
thinking about the teef of our dog. He don't need a nife to cut up
_dinner._     _gnaws through_
his diner. He just naws threw the meat.

## Did you notice every mistake?

It does not seem a good idea to watch television and do homework at the same time.

Amergit could think of the words, but certainly could not think of all the right spellings.

Did you correct all of his mistakes? If you missed any, think very carefully and use your other coloured pencil to make the corrections.

Last sumer a bilder came and put new cental heating in our house. Naturlly we was all very pleased because we new we would be warm in evry room when the winter came. The bilder and his men was very nice and Mum give them tea and biscits whenever they want them.

When the work was finshed the bilder gave my father a garantee for the job. We did not turn the heating on until last weak when it began to get colder. Then the hole house began to whisle. The niose was terrible. My father phoned the bilder to remind him about the garantee and get him to come and the whisle.

Unfortunatly the bilder is away on holday for thee weeks. We had to choose between keeping the whisle or being cold. We desided we would rather be cold!

summer  builder                    central
Last sumer a bilder came and put new cental heating in our
Naturally    were                          knew
house. Naturlly we was all very pleased because we new we
                          every                          builder
would be warm in evry room when the winter came. The bilder
          were                          gave                    biscuits
and his men was very nice and Mum give them tea and biscits
          wanted
whenever they want them.
                    finished    builder
    When the work was finshed the bilder gave my father a
guarantee
garantee for the job. We did not turn the heating on until last
week                                          whole
weak when it began to get colder. Then the hole house began to
whistle.      noise                              builder
whisle. The niose was terrible. My father phoned the bilder to
                    guarantee                          stop
remind him about the garantee and get him to come and ʌ the
whistle.
whisle.
    Unfortunately    builder            holiday    three
    Unfortunatly the bilder is away on holday for thee weeks.
                                          whistle
We had to choose between keeping the whisle or being cold.
    decided
We desided we would rather be cold!


## Did you notice every mistake?

It was certainly bad luck for Olivia and her family that the weather turned cold when the builder was away.

Let us hope he can stop the whistle quickly on his return. Perhaps when Olivia writes the next part of this story she will be able to spell builder and whistle.

Did you notice her mistakes and correct them for her? If not, think very hard and about any others you missed. Then make the corrections.

The Editor

Dear Sir,

My father has just come back from Ostralia and he told us we was thortless to grumble about our droght. Sum parts of Ostralia have not seen rain for over a year!

That is ruff. They have know water for themselves and none for the sheep and cattle. The grarss is brown and there is nothing for the anmals to eat. They are all losing wait and will probly die.

We are lucker here than those peple in Ostalia.

Yours trully

Pat Popper

## 16. Pat Popper

---

The Editor

Dear Sir,

*Australia*

My father has just come back from Ostralia and he told us we

*were thoughtless*       *drought. Some*      *Australia*

was thortless to grumble about our droght. Sum parts of Ostralia

have not seen rain for over a year!

    *rough.*         *no*

That is ruff. They have know water for themselves and none

          *grass*

for the sheep and cattle. The grarss is brown and there is nothing

    *animals*            *weight*      *probably*

for the anmals to eat. They are all losing wait and will probly

die.

    *luckier*           *people  Australia.*

We are lucker here than those peple in Ostalia.

       *truly*

     Yours trully

     Pat Popper

## Did you notice every mistake?

I am sure the Editor would have found Pat's letter very interesting, but he would have corrected her spelling mistakes before he put it in the paper.

Did you correct them all? If not, think carefully about her particular errors and then write the words correctly with your other coloured pencil (not red).

33

It was my great grandmother's nintieth birthday on Saterday. There were for genrations at her party. I had never met some of the older reltions before because they live in forign countries. But my cousins, brother, sister and me all had thorohly good time.

My mother had made a gygantic birthday so that it was big enuff for ninty candle. All of us of the younger genrations helpd great grandma blow them out. The other three genrations sang Happy Birthday.

While Mum and my aunty were cuting the cake, a mesnger came with a beatiful bunch of chrysanthmums. My uncle and his famly who live in Ostralia had arraged for them to be sent to great grandma. She was definitly thrill.

It was my great grandmother's *ninetieth* nintieth birthday on *Saturday.* Saterday.

There were *four generations* for genrations at her party. I had never met some of

the older *relations* reltions before because they live in *foreign* forign countries. But

my cousins, brother, sister and me all had ∧ *a thoroughly* thorohly good time.

My mother had made a *gigantic* gygantic birthday ∧ *cake* so that it was big

*enough* enuff for *ninety* ninty *candles.* candle. All of us of the younger *generations* genrations *helped* helpd

great grandma blow them out. The other three *generations* genrations sang

Happy Birthday.

While Mum and my aunty were *cutting* cuting the cake, a *messenger* mesnger

came with a *beautiful* beatiful bunch of *chrysanthemums.* chrysanthmums. My uncle and his

*family* famly who live in *Australia* Ostralia had *arranged* arraged for them to be sent to

great grandma. She was *definitely* definitly *thrilled.* thrill.

## Did you notice every mistake?

Rishi's great grandma certainly needed the help of the children to blow out 90 candles. It is sometimes hard to blow out 9, or 19 without help.

The mistakes with the spelling included some difficult words like <u>chrysanthemums</u>.

Did you spot those, as well as the mistakes with the easier words? Correct those you missed, thinking carefully.

I have just been on a visit to my new secondry school. I hope I will be going there next september. I thought the apperatus in the gymasium was marvellous. I am quiet a good gymast, so I shall look forward to using it.

The classrooms for gography and histry also looked particulerly intresting. There must be some good artits in the school because the picters were remarkeably good.

My sister is already the school and it might be awkwerd for my parents if I do not get in. Then we would have to go on seperate trains in diffrent direction and I no they would not like it.

## 18. Rachael Rogers

Wednesday, October 14th

secondary
I have just been on a visit to my new secondry school. I hope

September.        apparatus
I will be going there next september. I thought the apperatus in

gymnasium    marvellous.    quite    gymnast,
the gymasium was marvellous. I am quiet a good gymast, so I

shall look forward to using it.

geography    history
The classrooms for gography and histry also looked

particularly interesting.            artists
particulerly intresting. There must be some good artits in the

pictures    remarkably
school because the picters were remarkeably good.

at              awkward
My sister is already ∧ the school and it might be awkwerd for

my parents if I do not get in. Then we would have to go on

separate    different directions    know
seperate trains in diffrent direction and I no they would not

like it.

## Did you notice every mistake?

Rachael will have to wait a few months to see if she gets into the same school as her sister. Let us hope she does.

There are some words in the 'ar' family that she will need to look at carefully again, including secondary!

Did you notice all of her mistakes? Correct those you missed with your other coloured pencil.

My mother is quiet suspicous about our new next-door neghbors. A mysterous big black van come to their house quite late evry night and two big man get out with marsks round their faces. They manige to pull some gygantic boxes out of the van and carry them into the house next-door. Whatever is in those box, it smells atrocous. What could it be

On Saturday my mother said Im going to ring the plice. I am so anxous.

I shouldnt do that my father said. It could be awkwerd reporting on our negbors when they may not have done anything wrong.

Well, its mysterous and Im curous. I'll keep looking and smelling until I find out what is in those box, my mother replied.

*quite suspicious*
My mother is quiet suspicous about our new next-door
*neighbours.*   *mysterious*           *comes*
neghbors. A mysterous big black van come to their house quite
*every*          *men*        *masks*
late evry night and two big man get out with marsks round their
*manage*        *gigantic*
faces. They manige to pull some gygantic boxes out of the van

and carry them into the house next-door. Whatever is in those
*boxes,*       *atrocious.*
box, it smells atrocous. What could it be?
                    *"I'm*            *police.*
On Saturday my mother said, Im going to ring the plice.
*anxious."*
I am so anxous.
*shouldn't*                 *awkward*
"I shouldnt do that," my father said. "It could be awkwerd
*neighbours*
reporting on our negbors when they may not have done

anything wrong."
*it's mysterious*    *I'm curious.*
"Well, its mysterous and Im curous. I'll keep looking and
*boxes,"*
smelling until I find out what is in those box, my mother replied.

## Did you notice every mistake?

Would you be curious about those <u>gigantic</u>, smelly boxes? I think I would.

Simon made quite a few mistakes with the 'ous' family. He will need to go back to his word book and learn that family again.

Did you notice those errors – and the missing speech marks? Think hard about the mistakes you missed, then make the corrections.

Dear Sir,

All of the childrn in my class feel very misrable that the libry is going to close we need the libry for books on our projects these are not just ordnary books that we have at home or at school we always need particuler books about extrordinry subjects.

Do you have books in your house about Hungery, carniverous animals and conifrous trees if you do you are very fortunat and so are your children.

Yours sincerly

Terry Thompson

Dear Sir,

       *children*                     *miserable*       *library*

All of the childrn in my class feel very misrable that the libry

      *We*          *library*

is going to close. we need the libry for books on our projects.

*These*                *ordinary*

these are not just ordnary books that we have at home or at

      *We*          *particular*         *extraordinary*

school. we always need particuler books about extrordinry

subjects.

                          *Hungary, carnivorous*

Do you have books in your house about Hungery, carniverous

    *coniferous*      *If*               *fortunate*

animals and conifrous trees? if you do you are very fortunat and

so are your children.

    *sincerely*

Yours sincerly

Terry Thompson

# Did you notice every mistake?

Terry wrote a good letter to the local paper about the library closing.

Did the Brand's Patch teacher correct all of the mistakes before the letter was sent? Punctuation, capital letters and spellings, especially the word <u>library</u>, would have needed correction. What about <u>sincerely</u>? That is a tricky word.

Look carefully at the errors missed and think hard as you correct them.

The ladys at the libary are very angry because on Saturday night some horribel people used red, green and markers to scrible all over the libry walls. The ladys have said that those people who done this atrocous thing are irresponsble and have no principels.

Some of my friends and me have told the libry ladys that we will be responsble for cleaning the mess of the walls. We hope to it on Friday after school.

ladies        library
The ladys at the libary are very angry because on Saturday

horrible                          blue
night some horribel people used red, green and ∧markers to

scribble         library         ladies
scrible all over the libry walls. The ladys have said that those

did      atrocious          irresponsible
people who done this atrocous thing are irresponsble and have

principles.
no principels.

I                    library ladies
Some of my friends and me have told the libry ladys that we

responsible                      off
will be responsble for cleaning the mess of the walls. We hope

do
to∧it on Friday after school.

## Did you notice every mistake?

Ursula and her friends will be doing a good job if they clean the library walls and the <u>ladies</u> will be very pleased with them.

Did you spot all of the spelling mistakes? Which other colour did you choose? Perhaps you moved <u>and</u> instead? As long as the sentence about the <u>horrible people</u> and the <u>markers</u> makes sense, your correction will be fine.

Did you spot other errors?

My mother has gone to work in a shop that sells stationary. I need never be desprate for note-book and pencil now, because she can bring them home her.

She saw the advertisment for the job in the local newpaper. They wanted somone who had worked in a shop before. they also wanted a charactor refrence. This was not a problem, but my mother was still very nervus when she went for the interview.

They did ofer her the job and we was very thriled for her.

stationery.
My mother has gone to work in a shop that sells stationary.
desperate    note-books    pencils
I need never be desprate for note-book and pencil now, because
with
she can bring them home ∧ her.
advertisement                              newspaper.
She saw the advertisment for the job in the local newpaper.
someone                                    They
They wanted somone who had worked in a shop before. they
character reference.
also wanted a charactor refrence. This was not a problem, but
nervous
my mother was still very nervus when she went for the interview.
offer                    were    thrilled
They did ofer her the job and we was very thriled for her.

## Did you notice every mistake?

It would seem that Victoria does a lot of writing and therefore needs things from the <u>stationers</u>.

What spelling mistakes did she make?

Did you notice those and the other errors? If you missed any, think carefully as you make the corrections.

A mysterous germ has been going round my famly and at last the docter has been to visit us to talk about the simptoms. He brought with him a syring and some nasty syrep. When he had finshed asking us lot of questions, he used the syring to put some nasty syrep down our throtes. Im not shore what good that was meant do.

But to the suprise of all my famly, the simptoms disapeared and the mysterous germ has now gone away whatver was in the nasty syrep, it was obvously what we needed.

*mysterious* *family*
A mysterous germ has been going round my famly and at last
*doctor* *symptoms.*
the docter has been to visit us to talk about the simptoms. He
*syringe* *syrup.*
brought with him a syring and some nasty syrep. When he had
*finished* *lots* *questions,* *syringe*
finshed asking us lot of questions, he used the syring to put
*syrup* *throats.* *I'm* *sure*
some nasty syrep down our throtes. Im not shore what good
*to*
that was meant ∧ do.
*surprise* *family,* *symptoms disappeared*
But to the suprise of all my famly, the simptoms disapeared
*mysterious* *Whatever*
and the mysterous germ has now gone away. whatver was in the
*syrup,* *obviously*
nasty syrep, it was obvously what·we needed.

## Did you notice every mistake?

Wendy's doctor obviously discovered a lot about the mysterious germ by asking questions, so he knew how to cure her family.

She made spelling mistakes with some difficult words like <u>syringe</u>, but also wth some easier words like <u>family</u>.

Did you spot them all? Think carefully about those you missed, as you make the corrections.

We are going acros to france next week on a school excersion, to see were the D-Day invassion of europe in 1944 took place. We have seen a lot on telvision and have read a lot of books about it, but it will be very exsiting to actully go to those beeches.

It might be possble for us to have some discusion about what it really felt like because the grandfarther of one of the boy at our school, was one of the first english soldiers to go across the Chanel. He is comeing with us.

If I had been a yung soldier in the 1940s, I think I would liked to belong to the Paratroop Divsion. Then I would come down by parachut with my tiny motorbike under my arm.

across   France                                    excursion,
We are going acros to france next week on a school excersion,
where                invasion    Europe
to see were the D-Day invassion of europe in 1944 took place.
television
We have seen a lot on telvision and have read a lot of books
exciting    actually
about it, but it will be very exsiting to actully go to those
beaches.
beeches.
possible                          discussion
It might be possble for us to have some discusion about what
grandfather              boys
it really felt like because the grandfarther of one of the boy at
English
our school, was one of the first english soldiers to go across the
Channel.        coming
Chanel. He is comeing with us.
young                                      have
If I had been a yung soldier in the 1940s, I think I would ∧ liked
Division.              have
to belong to the Paratroop Divsion. Then I would ∧ come down by
parachute
parachut with my tiny motorbike under my arm.

## Did you notice every mistake?

The Brand's Patch children must have found the <u>excursion</u> to France very interesting, especially as a grandfather who had been there on D-Day was able to go with them.

Rex will need to look again at the words in the 'sion' family.

Did you notice those mistakes — and others? If you missed any, think hard and make the corrections with your other coloured pencil.

My parnts recieved a breif letter yesterday informing them that a supermarkit is going to be bilt on the field behind our house. At first they could not belief what they was reading. Then there was a knok at the door.

Our neihbour had also recieved a letter, so that had to belive that it was treu.

My father said fercely, Why was there no discusion with us We will here the nose of the lorries and cars every day of the weak.

I agree said our neibour. What they have done is really quiet decietful – to give permision without telling us.

I expet somone has recieved a lot of money my mother said.

She is pobably right, said my father.

parents received   brief
My parnts recieved a breif letter yesterday informing them
supermarket                    built
that a supermarkit is going to be bilt on the field behind our
believe              were
house. At first they could not belief what they was reading. Then
knock
there was a knok at the door.
neighbour              received                    they        believe
Our neihbour had also recieved a letter, so that∧had to belive
true
that it was treu.
fiercely,                              discussion
My father said fercely, "Why was there no discusion with us?
hear      noise
We will here the nose of the lorries and cars every day of the
week."
weak.
neighbour.
"I agree" said our neibour. "What they have done is really
quite deceitful              permission .
quiet decietful — to give permision without telling us."
expect someone     received
"I expet somone has recieved a lot of money," my mother said.
probably
"She is pobably right," said my father.

## Did you notice every mistake?

Did you put in all of the speech marks that were left out? If you missed any, think carefully about what the people are actually saying. That will help. What about the spelling mistakes?

Did you spot them all?

The dialy papers say that there will soon be elctions for parlament. I suppose that there will be an announcment and then evryone will start writting and talking about it.

I no my two brothers will have lots of fiece argumants. They suport diffrent parties, even though they are not old enuff to vote. I don't think they have sufficent experence to even talk about these things.

I lisen to their disussions, but I will make my own decisons when the time comes for me to vote.

daily

elections

The dialy papers say that there will soon be elctions for

parliament.

announcement

parlament. I suppose that there will be an announcment and

everyone        writing

then evryone will start writting and talking about it.

know

fierce arguments.

I no my two brothers will have lots of fiece argumants. They

support different

enough

suport diffrent parties, even though they are not old enuff to

sufficient experience

vote. I don't think they have sufficent experence to even talk

about these things.

listen        discussions,

decisions

I lisen to their disussions, but I will make my own decisons

when the time comes for me to vote.

## Did you notice every mistake?

Good for Zoe! She has to wait a few years before she can vote, but she has already decided to make her own <u>decisions</u> and not be influenced by her older brothers.

What about her spelling mistakes? There were not too many, but did you spot them all? Think carefully about those you missed and then make the corrections.

My grandma has decide to hold a specal famly occason on November 5th. I think she must have forget that this will be Bonfire Night. My parnts dont like to say anythink that mite offnd her, so we will all go.

Grandma lives in a flat in centrl London and cant possbly let us have firworks. My brother and I is not happy about it. Usully Firwork Night is a very specal socal occason and we meet lots of our friends at the huge bonfier in the park. There is lots of fierworks and it is great fun. We will miss it all this year.

## 27. Annie Andrews

---

*decided*    *special family occasion*
My grandma has decide to hold a specal famly occason on
*forgotten*
November 5th. I think she must have forget that this will be
*parents don't*    *anything*    *might*
Bonfire Night. My parnts dont like to say anythink that mite
*offend*
offnd her, so we will all go.

*central*    *can't possibly*
Grandma lives in a flat in centrl London and cant possbly let
*fireworks.*    *are*
us have firworks. My brother and I is not happy about it.
*Usually Firework*    *special social occasion*
Usully Firwork Night is a very specal socal occason and we meet
*bonfire*    *are*
lots of our friends at the huge bonfier in the park. There is lots of
*fireworks*
fierworks and it is great fun. We will miss it all this year.

## Did you notice every mistake?

Perhaps Annie's grandma had a surprise <u>firework</u> party arranged for them in a London park?

Even though Annie is unhappy, she has not made too many spelling mistakes. She will need to think carefully about <u>fireworks</u>, because she did not get that right at all.

Did you spot the other errors.

I have a bycycle and my little sister is going to have a trycycle for Christmas my father says that we can then go on cicle rides together. I think that that might be difficult because she will have to ride the trycicle on the pavment and I cicle on the road.

I think it would worry me. Things could go ary if she bumped into ladys on the pavment. I might wobbel into the trafic on the road because I will be look at her and not at the cars.

I have not said anythink to my father yet, but I will befor Christmas.

## 28. Bill Brown — Wednesday, November 4th

bicycle | tricycle
I have a bycycle and my little sister is going to have a trycycle

My | cycle
for Christmas. my father says that we can then go on cicle rides

together. I think that that might be difficult because she will have

tricycle | pavement | will cycle
to ride the trycicle on the pavment and I˄cicle on the road.

awry
I think it would worry me. Things could go ary if she bumped

ladies | pavement. | wobble | traffic
into ladys on the pavment. I might wobbel into the trafic on the

looking
road because I will be look at her and not at the cars.

anything | before
I have not said anythink to my father yet, but I will befor

Christmas.

### Did you notice every mistake?

Bill is wise to have a good chat with his father <u>before</u> Christmas about his worries.

He will need to look at the <u>cycle</u> family again.

Did you notice the mistakes and correct them? Think hard about any you missed and correct them with your other coloured pencil.

We are planing to have a beatiful Bonfire Night tonigt and lots of our fiends is comeing. The bonfire will be at the bottom of the garden, so we shall all easly be able to wach. Lots of rubish has been colleted and we have mixed that with piles of dry leafs.

Insted of Guy Fawkes we have made a creater of nilon and pliwood that looks like an egle. He is on top of the bonfire now, flaping his wings in the wind. Evry year we try to think of somethink knew to make. It just makes it all the more intresting.

My father has chosen the fireworks. He says that they will be exiting and beatiful, but safe! After the firworks, we will all go inside for super.

planning                beautiful                  tonight
We are planing to have a beatiful Bonfire Night tonigt and

friends are coming.
lots of our fiends is comeing. The bonfire will be at the bottom of

easily              watch.          rubbish
the garden, so we shall all easly be able to wach. Lots of rubish

collected                                          leaves.
has been colleted and we have mixed that with piles of dry leafs.

Instead                          creature   nylon
Insted of Guy Fawkes we have made a creater of nilon and

plywood                  eagle.
pliwood that looks like an egle. He is on top of the bonfire now,

flapping                      Every
flaping his wings in the wind. Evry year we try to think of

something  new                                    interesting.
somethink knew to make. It just makes it all the more intresting.

My father has chosen the fireworks. He says that they will be

exciting      beautiful,                    fireworks,
exiting and beatiful, but safe! After the firworks, we will all go

supper.
inside for super.

## Did you notice every mistake?

The <u>eagle</u> must have been fun to make. Let us hope he does not fly off into the wind before they light the bonfire!

Carole did not make too many mistakes.

Did you spot all of them – and make the corrections? Think very hard about those you missed.

Bonfire Night was horible for our neighbours because of the behavour of a gang that lives in the neighbourhod. Rumurs had been going round that this dishonorable gang was planing some wicked mischeif and evryone was hopping that it would not be there famly that sufered.

At about nine o'clock this retched gang soaked some peices of old towl in petrol and through them into the garden. After this they did somethink dredful and very dangerus. They lit some fireworks and through them on top of the old towls. Sudenly there was explosons and a mass of flames. The vapor from the petrol gave off a dreadful smell.

My father looked out of the window wen he heard the noise. He give a shout and immediatly rang 999 for the plice and fire-brigade. He went next-door to see our neighbour. Fortunatly the plice and fire engine come quickly. The fireman put out the fire and the police caught

horrible
Bonfire Night was horible for our neighbours because of the

behaviour                                    neighbourhood. Rumours
behavour of a gang that lives in the neighbourhod. Rumurs had

dishonourable                planning
been going round that this dishonorable gang was planing some

mischief      everyone        hoping
wicked mischeif and evryone was hopping that it would not be

their family      suffered.
there famly that sufered.

wretched                                  pieces
At about nine o'clock this retched gang soaked some peices of

towel              threw
old towl in petrol and through them into the garden. After this

something dreadful        dangerous.
they did somethink dredful and very dangerus. They lit some

threw                              towels. Suddenly
fireworks and through them on top of the old towls. Sudenly

were explosions                          vapour
there was explosons and a mass of flames. The vapor from the

petrol gave off a dreadful smell.

when
My father looked out of the window wen he heard the noise.

gave            immediately                    police
He give a shout and immediatly rang 999 for the plice and fire-

neighbours. Fortunately
brigade. He went next-door to see our neighbour. Fortunatly the

police              came              firemen
plice and fire engine come quickly. The fireman put out the fire

and the police caught the gang.

## Did you notice every mistake?

That will be a Bonfire Night that the Driver family will never forget.

This is a good piece of writing, but David has made some mistakes.

Did you miss any? Think carefully about those errors and correct them with your other coloured pencils.

An aquaintance of my mother is being a bit of a nusance at the moment. She is not a freind, but she thinks she is. She has just back come to Brands Patch to live and evry day she comes to our house for coffee. Somtimes my mother pretend she is out and does open the door.

Then my mother feels gilty because she is shure this lady needs assitance. She lives in very extravgant accommdation, but still seems very unhapy.

My father thinks she lives their for the apperance, not because she has got a lot of money, so she is probly very anxous about what she will do when the money runs out.

I think she got the money insorance and she has really got a lot. But she dose seem to be lonly and very short of frends and relatons.

acquaintance                                    nuisance
An aquaintance of my mother is being a bit of a nusance at

friend,
the moment. She is not a freind, but she thinks she is. She has

come back    Brand's                    every
just back come to Brands Patch to live and evry day she comes

Sometimes              pretends
to our house for coffee. Somtimes my mother pretend she is out

not
and does ∧ open the door.

guilty                    sure
Then my mother feels gilty because she is shure this lady

assistance.                    extravagant accommodation,
needs assitance. She lives in very extravgant accommdation, but

unhappy.
still seems very unhapy.

there          appearance,
My father thinks she lives their for the apperance, not because

probably    anxious
she has got a lot of money, so she is probly very anxous about

what she will do when the money runs out.

from insurance
I think she got the money ∧ insorance and she has really got a

does          lonely                    friends
lot. But she dose seem to be lonly and very short of frends and

relations.
relatons.


## Did you notice every mistake?

Like a lot of others in the purple class, Emily has made mistakes with difficult words, but certainly got the date right.

Did you notice her mistakes — and could you correct them with your red pencil? If you did miss any, take your other coloured pencil, think carefully and make the corrections.